The Od

VOLUME ONE

by Allan Plenderleith

ℛ
RAVETTE PUBLISHING

THE ODD SQUAD and all related characters
© 1997 by Allan Plenderleith
www.theoddsquad.co.uk

All rights reserved

First Published by Ravette Publishing Limited 1997
Reprinted 1999

This book is sold subject to the condition that
it shall not, by way of trade or otherwise, be
lent, resold, hired out or otherwise circulated
without the publisher's prior consent in any
form of binding or cover other than that in
which this is published and without a similar
condition including this condition being
imposed on the subsequent purchaser.

Printed and bound for
Ravette Publishing Limited,
Unit 3, Tristar Centre, Star Road,
Partridge Green, West Sussex RH13 8RA

email: ravettepub@aol.com
website: www.ravettepub.co.uk

by Proost, Belgium

ISBN: 1 85304 936 0

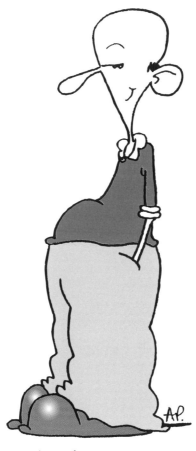

To Mum, Dad
Laura & Rebeccah

Jeff makes a cat flap

No-one would forget that day - when a sudden gust of wind 'snatched' all trainspotters wearing hoods

At the cash dispenser, Dug opts for "CASH – WITH ADVICE"

Maude's boyfriend gives her multiple organisms

Once again, Jeff had to work late
because they were short-staffed

Nose hairs aren't meant to be trimmed — but grown and used as antennae

Although the man claimed he was a
"Fish Collector for the Homeless"
— Jeff had his suspicions

So that __was__ where the gerbil had got to

It wasn't so much the poo in his slipper that bothered Jeff - more the smirk on his dog's face

Far from saggy boobs being a burden, they can become handy holders for cigarettes and pencils

Jeff's girlfriend is a fat ugly cow

Vicious traps, poison, mouldy cheese-
clearly, this madman had to be stopped

To decide who buys the first round,
Dug and his friends draw straws

Billy's rabbit becomes the ill-fated star of a You've Been Framed clip

Jeff's bath was too deep

He didn't care what anyone else said, Jeff loved his remote control and that was that

Although the survivors had no food and were miles from anywhere – they needn't worry – because Jeff had remembered the flares

Jeff's garden was always
full of toad stools

Tired of the endless offerings of nuts — this time the squirrels wanted meat!

Never sneeze while squeezing toothpaste

Jeff receives a large
Czech through the post

Clearly, during the night, the dog had discovered how to operate the pencil sharpener

Never underestimate a hamster

Jeff enters a
'go for another wipe or leave it'
dilemma

Billy learns about proper and abstract nuns

Maude locked her shelf out again

While clearing out the fridge,
Jeff finds Elvis Presley

As a louder and more satisfying alternative to clapping, Lily slaps together the loose skin under her arms

Someone had sharpened the strings
on Jeff's guitar

After repeated banging and a loud 'crack', Jeff's door finally closed

Jeff knew his dog was healthy
because he had a lovely wet nose

During the disco, Maude finds an embarrassing ladder in her tights

The transition from girl to woman
is both sudden and disturbing

Maude loves to go scooby diving

Jeff loved a good book

Jeff and his neighbour secretly hold an illegal pillow fight

Jeff loves going north of the border

Once again, Jeff was overdrawn

Jeff wasn't feeling himself

Papercuts are never pleasant

Jeff gives them the wrong impression

Jeff decides not to buy
a double-breasted suit

Maude clears out all the old
embarrassing stuff from her wardrobe

Jeff had an annoying
hare in his mouth

During the night, somebody had replaced Jeff's limbs with selected root vegetables

Jeff is surprised to find a small squirrel in his belly button

Jeff teaches his dog never to poo on the bed again

While going through one of his old jackets, Jeff finds four million pounds

Having sacrificed his entire social life for the last 3 years by studying, Dug's efforts finally bear fruit

Never blow-off wearing a g-string

To create more impact when entering the pub, Jeff plays his own theme tune

Every Saturday night,
Maude gets stoned

Jobby-related stress

Billy and Moira carry out a hardness test on Cyril

Once again, Dug used too much
tippex during the exam

Although they'd lost both wings
Dug brings the plane down safely
with his 70's style lapels

Using some lipstick on her double chin, Lily scares the children with her 'extra mouth' routine

Having waited 17 hours after his 999 call, Jeff realised he'd actually called St. John's ambience

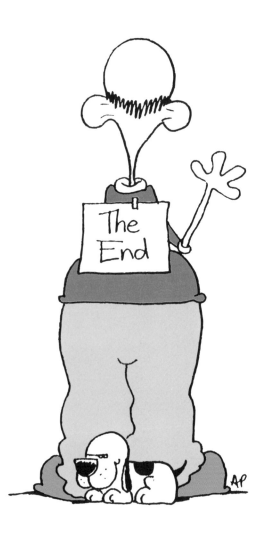